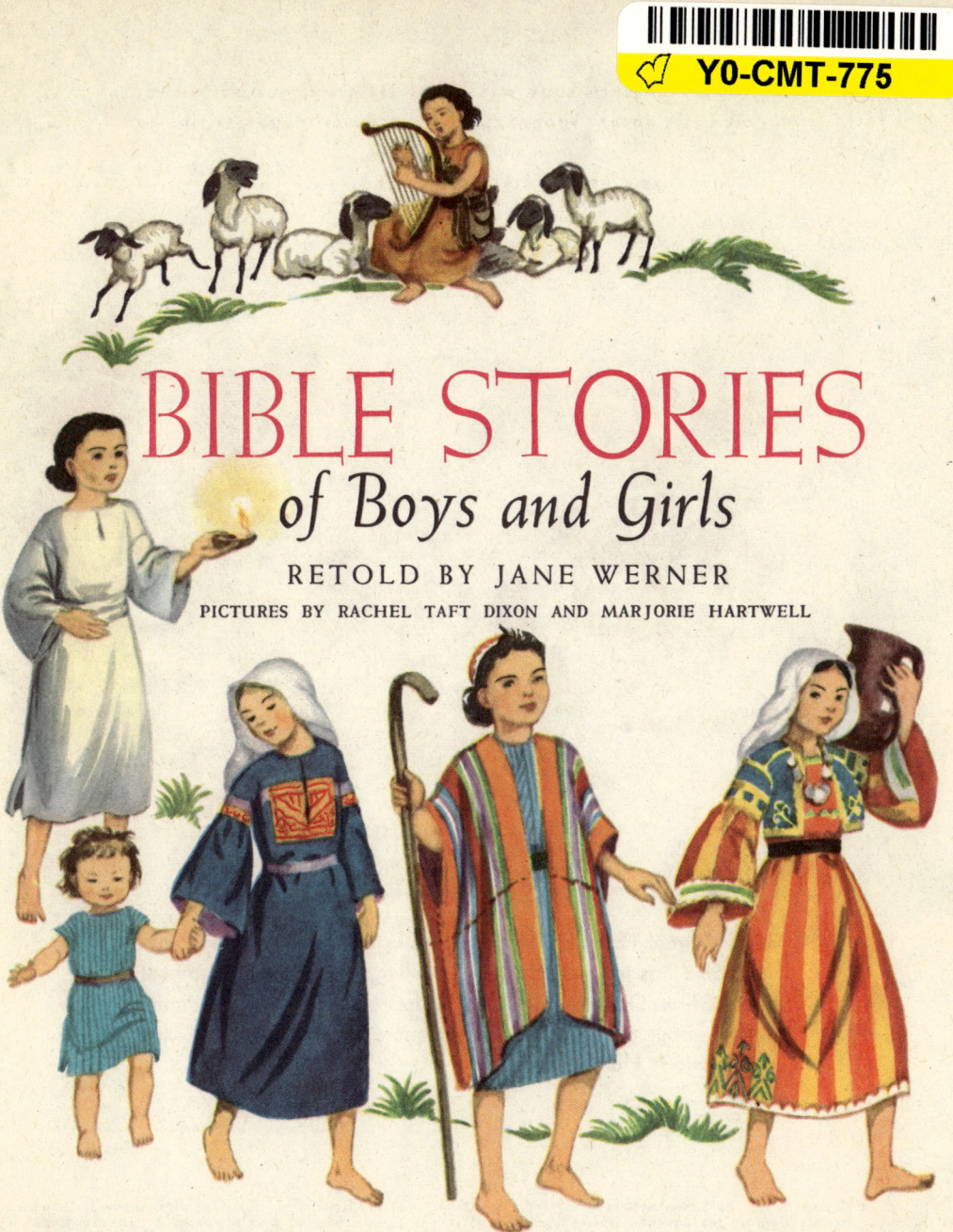

BIBLE STORIES
of Boys and Girls

RETOLD BY JANE WERNER
PICTURES BY RACHEL TAFT DIXON AND MARJORIE HARTWELL

SIMON AND SCHUSTER · NEW YORK

THIS IS A BRAND-NEW BOOK, ILLUSTRATED ESPECIALLY FOR GOLDEN BOOKS
THE LITTLE GOLDEN BOOKS ARE PRODUCED UNDER THE SUPERVISION OF
MARY REED, Ph.D.
FORMERLY OF TEACHERS COLLEGE, COLUMBIA UNIVERSITY

Author and Artist

Jane Werner has planned many books of bible stories for children, and has just completed a re-telling of the New Testament as a Giant Golden Book. Her adaptation of Old-Testament stories about children is here illustrated by Rachel Taft Dixon and Marjorie Hartwell.

Copyright 1953 by Simon and Schuster, Inc., and Artists and Writers Guild, Inc. All rights reserved, including the right of reproduction in whole or in part in any form. Designed and produced by The Sandpiper Press and Artists and Writers Guild, Inc. Printed in the U.S.A. by Western Printing and Lithographing Company. Published by Simon and Schuster, Inc., Rockefeller Center, New York 20, New York. Published simultaneously in Canada by the Musson Book Company, Ltd., Toronto

REBEKAH AT THE WELL

Rebekah was a girl who lived long ago in a sun-baked city on the plains. Each evening she went out with her pitcher on her shoulder to draw fresh water from the well.

One evening she met a stranger from afar sitting wearily at the well. He had made his camels kneel beside him, for they were tired and thirsty too.

"Let me please drink a little water from your pitcher," the stranger said to her.

"Drink, sir," said Rebekah, lowering her pitcher,

and she drew more water to fill the trough, so his camels could drink too.

"Is there room in your father's house for me to spend the night?" the stranger asked Rebekah then. It was the custom in those times to take traveling strangers in.

Rebekah led him to her father's house. And they made him welcome there.

When the man sat down to eat, he told his wonderful news. The Lord had sent him from afar to find a wife for a fine young man—a wife who should be both fair and kind. Now he knew that Rebekah was the girl the Lord had meant, because she had been so kind to him.

He brought out jewels of gold and silver—fine bracelets he put on Rebekah's arms. And he gave her family precious gifts, too. Because Rebekah had been chosen by the Lord.

JOSEPH AND HIS DREAMS

Joseph was the favorite son of his father. He had a coat of many colors, finer by far than any of his brothers had. His brothers did not like that.

When they all went out to feed their father's flocks, Joseph would go home and tell tales about the brothers. And they did not like that, you may be sure.

Then Joseph dreamed proud dreams in which he ruled over his brothers, and he told them all his dreams.

This made his brothers angrier than ever, and they plotted together against him.

One day when Joseph came out into the fields, wearing his many-colored coat, the hard-hearted brothers plotted to kill him. But two of them said,

"No. Let us sell him to this caravan from Gilead, going to Egypt with spices, balm and myrrh."

So proud young Joseph was sold as a slave. And many long years did he work and wait before he saw his brothers and his father again.

By then he had lost his foolish pride. He forgave them gladly and welcomed them. For do you know, his dream had come true, and he was a ruler in the land of Egypt, far from his boyhood home.

MIRIAM, THE GOOD SISTER

Bad times had come to the children of Israel. The hard-hearted ruler of the land of Egypt—the Pharaoh, he was called—wanted all boy babies killed.

Now a couple of the House of Levi had a son, and he was a fine sturdy boy. His mother hid him for three months, and when she could not hide him any longer, she took a covered basket of bulrushes, made it watertight with pitch, and laid the baby in it.

Then she put the little boat among the reeds by the river bank. And the baby's sister Miriam stood at a distance to watch over him.

The daughter of Pharaoh came down to bathe at the river, and saw the basket among the reeds. She sent her maid to fetch it, and when she opened it, she saw the baby, who began to cry.

She took pity on him, and decided to save him. "But someone must care for him," the princess said.

Then Miriam, who had been watching and listening, stepped bravely forward from her hiding place.

"Shall I bring a Hebrew woman to nurse the child for you?" she asked.

"Go," said Pharaoh's daughter, so Miriam ran and brought her own mother.

"Take care of the child and I will give you wages," Pharaoh's daughter said.

So the happy mother had her child back. Because his sister Miriam had watched over him, he grew up safe and sound at home.

When he was older, this boy Moses was educated in the palace of the king and became the greatest leader his people knew.

SAMUEL, THE LORD'S CHILD

Once there was a woman named Hannah who was sad at heart because she had no child.

She prayed to the Lord and promised him, "O Lord of hosts, if you send me a man-child, I will give him to the service of the Lord all the days of his life."

In due time Hannah had a son, and she called him Samuel.

When he was still very young, his mother took him to the house of the Lord—with three bulls and flour and wine for sacrifice. And she left her son to serve the Lord.

Each year Samuel's mother made him a little coat and brought it to him when she came with her husband to offer the yearly sacrifice. But Samuel lived in the temple there and was taught by Eli the priest.

One night when Samuel had lain down to sleep, the Lord called, "Samuel."

"Here I am," said Samuel, thinking Eli had called. And he ran to Eli's side.

But Eli said, "I did not call. Lie down again and sleep."

Three times the Lord called, "Samuel." And each time Samuel said, "Here I am," and ran to Eli's side.

At last Eli understood that it was the Lord who called, and he said, "Go, lie down, and if he calls again, say, 'Speak, Lord, for your servant is listening.'"

So the boy went and lay down in his place, and the Lord came and stood there and spoke to him, telling him all his plans for Samuel, who was to be a prophet of the Lord.

DAVID THE SHEPHERD KING

David, the youngest son of Jesse of Bethlehem, was out in the hills one day, tending his father's sheep. It was a lonely life, being a shepherd boy, but David did not mind. He had his harp, and he played sweet music and made up many songs.

There were dangers, too, wild animals lurking. But David was brave and strong. Once a lion attacked the sheep, and once a bear came and stole a lamb away. But David killed them both, the lion and the bear, and he kept his sheep all safe.

Now one of his brothers came over the hill to say he was wanted at home. David went along, with no thought of what was waiting for him.

It was Samuel, prophet of the Lord, who was there at his father's house.

"I have chosen one of Jesse's sons to be king," the Lord had told Samuel.

So Samuel came to Jesse's house, and Jesse brought out his seven tall sons.

When Samuel saw Eliab, the first, he said, "Surely this is the Lord's chosen one," For he was handsome and tall.

But the Lord said to Samuel, "I have not chosen him. Do not look at his face or the height of him. The Lord does not see as man sees.

"Man looks at the outward appearance, but the Lord looks at the heart."

Then Jesse called Abinadab, and made him stand before Samuel. But Samuel said, "The Lord has not chosen this one either."

Then Jesse made Shammah step forward, and each of the seven, but Samuel said, "No," to each. "The Lord has not chosen these," he said. "Are these all the sons you have?"

"There is still the youngest, David," Jesse said. "He is keeping the sheep."

"Fetch him here," said Samuel. And when the young boy David appeared, the Lord said to Samuel, "Arise, anoint him, for this is he who shall be king."

Then Samuel took the horn of oil and poured it upon David before his brothers. And the spirit of the Lord was with David from then on, because he was pure of heart.